Steven Croft

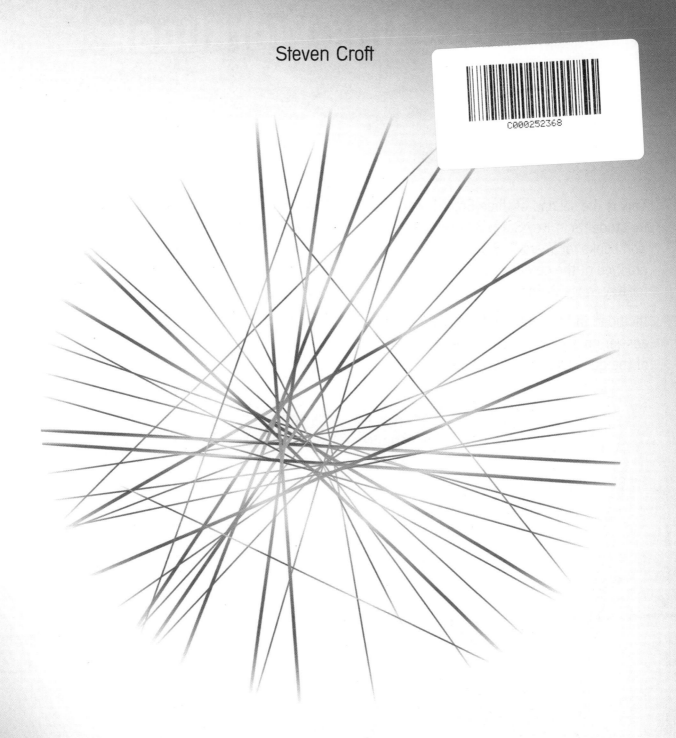

ESSENTIALS

Year 8
KS3 English
Workbook

How to Use this Workbook

A Note to the Teacher

This is the second of three English workbooks for students in Key Stage 3. Together, the workbooks for Years 7, 8 and 9 provide practice of the complete programme of study for Key Stage 3 English.

Included in the centre of the book is a pull-out answer booklet. It contains the answers to all of the questions in this workbook.

The topics covered in this workbook complement the KS3 Year 8 English Essentials Coursebook to provide further practice and help consolidate learning. The coursebooks provide clear, concise information as well as further practice questions.

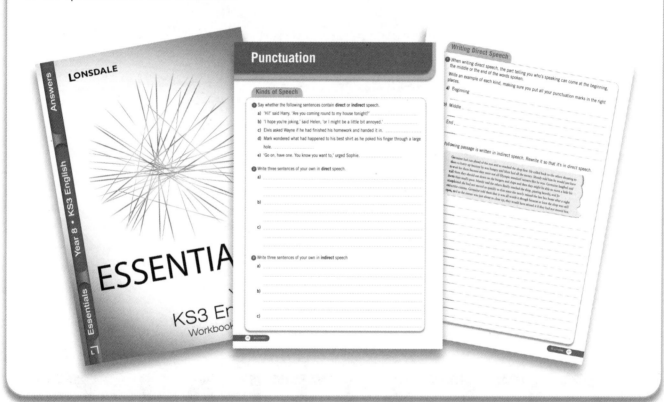

A Note to the Student

We're sure you'll enjoy using this workbook, but follow these helpful hints to make the most of it:

- Try to write your answers in Standard English, using correct punctuation and good sentence construction. Read what you have written to make sure it makes sense.

- Some questions will require extra research, using reference books like dictionaries, encyclopedias and thesauruses, or the use of the internet.
- The tick boxes on the Contents page let you track your progress: simply put a tick in the box next to each topic when you've completed the exercises and questions.

Contents

Imaginative Writing

Beginning a Story

Look at the beginnings of the following stories. How do the writers open their stories and what techniques do they use to create their effects?

a)

> Crash! The noise came from the next room, shattering the thick silence. It sounded like someone dropping a glass or a bottle. Silence again. I listened intently. Nothing. Then a floorboard creaked, then another. Someone was pacing the room. But I knew that could not be. I knew I was the only living thing in that house. Or was I?

b)

> The two cottages stood side by side at the foot of a hill, not far from a small spa town. The two peasant farmers who lived in them worked very hard cultivating the poor soil to rear all the children they had. Each couple had four, and outside each house the whole gang of them played and shrieked from morning till night. The oldest two were six and the youngest two about fifteen months.
>
> From *Country Living* by Guy de Maupassant

c)

> 'I want to go to heaven,' Donald said.
> 'You can't go to heaven today,' said Mum. 'It's Tuesday. Tuesdays I don't go to heaven, I go shopping.'
> 'I'll go with Dad, then.'
> 'Not today you won't. It's Dad's day for going to the hospital. He has to have his leg looked at.'
> 'Well, Kathy can take me.'
> 'You know very well Kathy can't take you. You don't go to heaven without me or Dad.'
>
> From *Top of the World* by John Rowe Townsend

Beginning a Story (Cont.)

d)

> Janna packed her books in her bag eagerly. She loved school. She always had, right from the start. English was her favourite subject and it was her ambition to become a journalist. Today was no ordinary day, though. It was the day when she was to receive the prize she had won in the school's story-writing competition. She was so excited that her hand trembled as she opened the door to her best friends, Sally and Binta, who had come to walk to school with her.

Developing Your Ideas

When planning a story of your own you need to think carefully about all the various things that make up the story.

Make a list of the things you need to think about in your story.

a)

b)

c)

d)

e)

f)

Narrative Style

Stories are usually written in either the **first person** or the **third person**.

Explain each kind of narration and the different effects they can have on how a story is told.

a) First person narration

b) Third person narration

Story Openings

Choose one of your favourite stories and write about how the story opens.

Use the following points to help express your ideas.

a) How the story opens.

b) Why you think the opening is effective.

c) Examples of ways in which the writer uses language.

d) What the opening vividly describes.

e) **i)** The narrative viewpoint.

ii) Why this narrative viewpoint is effective.

f) Your overall impression of the opening.

Writing Your Own Opening

Experiment with writing some opening paragraphs of your own.

a) Write an opening paragraph that uses a surprise or unexpected idea to capture the reader's attention. Write in either the first person or the third person.

b) Write an opening paragraph that launches straight into direct speech to capture the attention of the reader. Write in the first person.

c) Write an opening paragraph that begins by describing a character. Write in the third person.

d) Write an opening paragraph that begins by setting or describing the scene. Write in either the first person or the third person.

Planning Your Own Story

Write a detailed plan for a story of your own. Use the following headings to help structure your ideas.

a) The kind of story you're going to write. ....

b) The viewpoint you will use. ....

c) The characters in the story, with a brief outline saying who they are, etc.

....

....

....

d) A brief summary of the storyline in no more than fifty words.

....

....

....

....

e) How you will open the story.

....

....

f) The development (use a maximum of 10 bullet points).

....

....

....

....

....

....

....

g) The climax of the story.

....

....

Planning Your Own Story (Cont.)

h) How you will end your story.

Introducing Characters

Write three short character introductions of your own in different styles.

Experiment with alternative ways of introducing characters.

a) Using direct speech

b) Using first person narration

c) Using third person narration

Character and Atmosphere

Creating Characters

The following extracts describe various characters.

Write down your impressions of each character and pick two phrases or pieces of description that helped you to form your impressions.

a)

> "Hold your noise!" cried a terrible voice, as a man started up from among the graves at the side of the church porch. "Keep still, you little devil, or I'll cut your throat!"
>
> A fearful man, all in coarse grey, with a great iron on his leg. A man with no hat, and with broken shoes, and with an old rag tied round his head. A man who had been soaked in water, and smothered in mud, and lamed by stones, and cut by flints, and stung by nettles, and torn by briars; who limped, and shivered, and glared, and growled; and whose teeth chattered in his head as he seized me by the chin.
> "Oh! Don't cut my throat, sir," I pleaded in terror. "Pray don't do it, sir."
> "Tell us your name!" said the man. "Quick!"
>
> From *Great Expectations* by Charles Dickens

    i) Impressions of the character

    ....

    ....

    ii) Phrases that helped you to form your impressions

    ....

    ....

b)

> Mr Ellis was standing behind his desk, not sitting, and he looked like a dirty great thundercloud. He was big, dead big, and horrible-looking, with monster shoulders like Frankenstein, and all this bushy black hair. Big black eyebrows, too, that stuck out far enough to put things on. His eyes, underneath them, glittered, in the second that Bernard managed to look at them.
>
> From *My Mate Shofiq* by Jan Needle

    i) Impressions of the character

    ....

    ....

    ii) Phrases that helped you to form your impressions

    ....

    ....

Making Characters Come To Life

1 List eight ways in which writers can give you a strong impression of their characters and make them believable.

a)

b)

c)

d)

e)

f)

g)

h)

2 Now go back to the story you began planning in the last section and think about the main character you created. Complete the following sections, giving details about your character.

a) Character's name.

b) Background details.

c) Physical appearance.

d) What they do in the story.

e) How they relate to other characters.

f) What other characters think about them.

Settings

As well as the characters creating a vivid impression, the setting of your story can be important too. Look at the following passage and answer the questions that follow.

'All right, back there?' said Maria's father.

'Not much longer now,' said Maria's mother.

Neither of them turned round. The backs of their heads rode smoothly forward between the landscapes that unrolled at either side of the car; hedges, trees, fields, houses that came and went before there was time to examine them. Fields with corn. Fields with animals. From time to time, on the left, snatches of a milky green sea bordered with a ribbon of golden sand or shingle. That is the English Channel, said Maria, inside her head, to the ashtray on the back of the car seat, the sea. We have come to spend our summer holiday beside it, because that is what people do. You go down to the beach everyday and run about and shout and build sandcastles and all that. You have blown-up rubber animals and iced lollies and there is sand in your bed at night. You do that in August. As far as I know everybody in the world does.

From *A Stitch in Time* by Penelope Lively

a) How do the opening two lines help to create the setting?

....

....

b) i) How does the writer create an impression of what they see from the car windows as they are travelling?

....

....

ii) Give a specific example of what they see.

....

c) What is the effect of the writer's use of the word 'unrolled'?

....

....

d) i) How does the writer use the thoughts in Maria's head to set the scene?

....

....

ii) Give an example of Maria's thoughts.

....

....

Atmosphere

1. Write down all the different kinds of atmosphere you can think of. Two suggestions are given to start you off.

spooky; sad

2. Choose three very different kinds of atmospheres from your list. Write a short paragraph for each one in which you capture the chosen atmosphere. Say which atmosphere you're trying to create at the beginning of each one.

a) Atmosphere:

Paragraph:

b) Atmosphere:

Paragraph:

c) Atmosphere:

Paragraph:

Grammar

Word Classes

Complete the following table by listing all the word classes. Give a short explanation for each one and then give an example. The first one has been done for you.

Word Classes	Explanation	Example
Noun	A word that names something	Table

Word Classes in Action

Look at the following sentences and identify the word classes by writing the names of each one in the boxes.

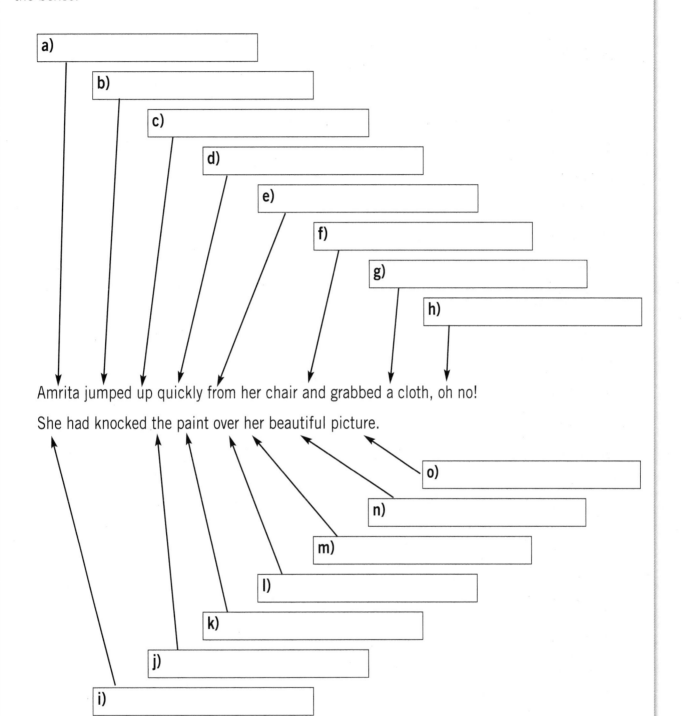

a)

b)

c)

d)

e)

f)

g)

h)

Amrita jumped up quickly from her chair and grabbed a cloth, oh no!

She had knocked the paint over her beautiful picture.

o)

n)

m)

l)

k)

j)

i)

Types of Nouns

Look at the list of nouns below and say what type of noun they are. They are either **abstract**, **collective**, **proper** or **common** nouns. The first one has been done for you.

a) Durham   *Proper*

b) Shoal

c) Jealousy

d) Planet

e) Mario

f) Anger

g) Village

h) Desk

i) Queue

j) River Avon

k) Fence

l) Telephone

m) School

n) Music

o) Love

p) Squad

q) Scotland

r) Mathematics

s) Pencil

t) Natalie

u) Newspaper

v) Happiness

w) Town

x) Book

y) Shakespeare

z) Sadness

Identifying Word Classes

Read the following passage and look at the word classes.

List the **pronouns, prepositions, conjunctions** and **articles** below. When identifying articles, say whether they are **definite** or **indefinite** articles.

The wind howled continuously across the bleak moor and, as darkness fell, Tom and his friends began to feel more and more uneasy. They had not seen any landmarks that they recognised for some time now and what had seemed like a clear path when they turned off the main track after they had left the ruined farmhouse was now barely visible at all. Turning back was an option, but finding their way back to the farm was not as simple as it might sound because, now that the light was almost gone, they only had the light from their torches to rely on. Things were looking bleak and, to put the finishing touches on the situation, the first large drops of rain began to fall on them and they heard a low rumble of thunder away in the distance.

a) Pronouns

b) Prepositions

c) Conjunctions

d) Articles (definite and indefinite)

Audience and Purpose

Purpose

Below are some general purposes for writing.

List four different kinds of writing under each heading. Give the specific purpose for each of your examples. Some ideas have been given to help you get started.

a) To **entertain / describe**, e.g. A ghost story. Purpose: to entertain and maybe frighten. Will probably describe too.

   i) ....

   ii) ....

   iii) ....

   iv) ....

b) To **argue / persuade**, e.g. a Greenpeace leaflet. Purpose: to persuade

   i) ....

   ii) ....

   iii) ....

   iv) ....

c) To **inform / advise**, e.g. information leaflet in the local library

   i) ....

   ii) ....

   iii) ....

   iv) ....

d) To **complain / explain**, e.g. a leaflet explaining how to look after a guinea pig

   i) ....

   ii) ....

   iii) ....

   iv) ....

Purpose and Audience

Look at the following examples of various kinds of writing. Write down what you think the audience and purpose for each one is.

a)

> Hi Mum,
>
> I won't be in for tea tonight. Becky and I are off to the cinema when we've finished shopping.
>
> See you later,
>
> Love
>
> Mandy

i) Audience

ii) Purpose

b)

> Humpty Dumpty sat on a wall,
> Humpty Dumpty had a great fall.
> All the King's horses and all the King's men,
> Couldn't put Humpty together again.

i) Audience

ii) Purpose

c)

> Henry VIII was the third child of Henry VII and Elizabeth of York. He was born in Greenwich Palace and only three of his six brothers and sisters survived beyond infancy – Arthur, Margaret and Mary. Henry was appointed Constable of Dover Castle and Lord Warden of the Cinque Ports in 1493 and the year after this he became the Duke of York.

i) Audience

ii) Purpose

Types of Writing

From your experience of different types of writing, think about how different types vary depending on their purpose and the audience they're aimed at.

Look at the following examples of different writing types and give two ideas about how you would expect each one to be written.

The first one has been done for you to get you started.

a) An entry about France in an encyclopaedia, aimed at children aged 8–10 years.

    i) The language would need to be quite simple and straightforward; chosen to suit young children of about 8–10.

    ii) The information would need to be easy to read and understand, and quite brief, dealing with the key points.

b) A leaflet about how to look after a pet rabbit.

    i) ....

    ....

    ii) ....

    ....

c) A review of a computer game.

    i) ....

    ....

    ii) ....

    ....

d) An extract from a travel brochure.

    i) ....

    ....

    ii) ....

    ....

e) An advertisement for a mobile phone.

    i) ....

    ....

    ii) ....

Writing Short Pieces

Write three short pieces of writing aimed at different types of audiences and with specific purposes.

Say what the audience and purpose is for each of your pieces of writing.

a) Audience: .... Purpose: ....

....

....

....

....

....

....

....

b) Audience: .... Purpose: ....

....

....

....

....

....

....

....

c) Audience: .... Purpose: ....

....

....

....

....

....

....

....

....

Developing a Point of View

Points of View

a) List five techniques you could use when writing to put your point of view across effectively to your reader.

i) ....

ii) ....

iii) ....

iv) ....

v) ....

b) Give an example of each of these techniques in a sentence or short paragraph of your own. Describe the effects you have created.

i) ....

....

....

ii) ....

....

....

iii) ....

....

....

iv) ....

....

....

v) ....

....

Fact and Opinion

1 Look at these sentences and say whether they are **fact** or **opinion**.

a) Paris is the capital of France.

b) A robin is a kind of bird.

c) Mowing the lawn is hard work.

d) Shakespeare wrote plays.

e) All Wordsworth's poems are very good.

f) Writing stories is easy.

g) School is there to provide you with a good education.

h) The painting was wonderful.

i) Many people enjoy listening to the music of Mozart.

j) Manchester United has won many trophies.

k) *Hollyoaks* is a brilliant TV programme.

l) Fishing is a really interesting hobby.

2 Sometimes writers use a mixture of fact and opinion in their writing. Look at the following sentences and identify the facts and opinions in each.

a) Many years ago Paul McCartney was a member of The Beatles but he still writes good songs today.

   i) Fact: ....

   ii) Opinion: ....

b) Margaret Thatcher was the first female Prime Minister and did a fantastic job of running the country.

   i) Fact: ....

   ii) Opinion: ....

c) Charles I was executed because he listened to the advice of fools.

   i) Fact: ....

   ii) Opinion: ....

d) Shakespeare wrote *Macbeth* and it is his best play.

   i) Fact: ....

   ii) Opinion: ....

e) Science is an important subject and easily the most enjoyable.

   i) Fact: ....

   ii) Opinion: ....

Writing Fact and Opinion

1 Choose any subject and write a factual account or description of it. Make sure that all the information you give is factual.

_____

_____

_____

_____

_____

_____

_____

_____

_____

_____

_____

2 Write an account that is based entirely on your own opinions rather than facts. You can use the same subject as in question 1, or choose a different one.

_____

_____

_____

_____

_____

_____

_____

_____

_____

_____

_____

_____

Writing Techniques

Carefully read the following letter from a local newspaper, in which the writer puts across her views on the bus service in her area.

Dear Editor

I am writing to protest about the withdrawal of the bus service from Sombourne to Egbury. This latest cut in services will mean that there will be no bus service to connect the village of Sunnyvale to the two nearest towns. Has any consideration been given to the people who live in this village? Has any consideration been given to all the people who live along the rest of the route? I doubt it. I doubt if the people who make these plans and decisions have given any thought to all the people who will be affected by this cut in service, otherwise they would never have made this thoughtless decision. More than three hundred and fifty people live in Sunnyvale and at least another two hundred on the route between Sombourne and Egbury.

The Reliance Bus Company have said that most people have cars. This may be true but not everyone has a car. For the elderly and young people like myself who are not old enough to drive, the bus is the only way we have to get to town to shop, meet friends, go to the cinema and so on. The cutting of this service will mean we become prisoners, trapped in our village! There is nothing to do here, and so more people will end up hanging about on street corners and vandalism is bound to increase. Is this what the council and Reliance Buses want? If not, change this ridiculous decision now!

Yours sincerely,

A. Smith

Identify the underlined techniques that the writer used to put her viewpoint across to the reader.

a) ....

....

b) ....

....

c) ....

....

d) ....

....

e) ....

....

Presenting Your Own Views

Write your own piece in which you present your views on a particular topic. Imagine you're writing a letter to protest or complain about something. Use the following to help you structure your piece.

a) Choose the topic you're going to write about. Write your topic below.

_____

b) Write the opening sentence.

_____

_____

c) Write your opening paragraph.

_____

_____

_____

_____

d) Write two more paragraphs, which will form the main body of your letter.

Paragraph 1:

_____

_____

_____

_____

Paragraph 2:

_____

_____

_____

_____

e) Write your concluding paragraph. Make sure that it has some kind of impact.

_____

_____

_____

_____

Presenting Information

Writing to Inform

1. Fill in the table with ten different kinds of informative writing that are presented in different ways.

   Give an example of each kind. The first one has been done for you.

Kind of Information	Example
Text book	A book on geography for lower secondary students
a)	
b)	
c)	
d)	
e)	
f)	
g)	
h)	
i)	

2. What do all these kinds of writing have in common?

_____

_____

_____

Informative Writing

Choose the correct words from the options given to complete the sentences below.

heading	writing	bold	special	blank
fonts	different	colour	paragraphs	aid
text	columns	sub-headings	cap	sizes
bullet	italics	photographs	plans	diagrams

a) The main title of a piece of informative writing is often called the _____ .

b) Sometimes _____ print is used to emphasise particular points.

c) The different styles of lettering are called _____ .

d) Letters can be printed in different _____ to achieve different effects.

e) The writing is called the _____ .

f) Secondary titles are called _____ .

g) The use of _____ can make brochures and leaflets more eye-catching.

h) Pieces of information can be presented using _____ points to make it easier to understand.

i) Sometimes _____ can be used to draw attention to particular words and phrases.

j) _____ and _____ are sometimes used to illustrate or explain the text.

LONSDALE

ESSENTIALS

Year 8
KS3 English
Workbook Answers

IMAGINATIVE WRITING

Page 4–7

Beginning a Story

a) A sudden 'shock' type opening, followed by the creation of a sense of mystery. This captures the reader's interest and keeps them guessing and wanting to read on to find out what's happening.

b) A brief description of the setting and an introduction to some of the characters.

c) Direct speech is used and the conversation arouses the reader's curiosity, especially the reference to 'heaven'.

d) Information is given about the character and situation.

Developing Your Ideas

a)–f) **Any suitable ideas, for example**: How to begin your story; how the events of your story will link together; how you will structure your story; how you will keep your reader interested; how you're going to present your characters; what the setting of your story will be; what the climax of your story will be; how you will end your story.

Narrative Style

a) The narrator is a character in the story and it's told from the 'I' viewpoint. This gives the impression that the narrator is addressing the reader directly. Everything is seen from the point of view of the narrator.

b) The narrator is outside the novel and describes the characters and events as if they know everything that is going on. They can describe what is going on in the minds of all the characters and make comments on characters and events.

Story Openings

a) Look carefully at the techniques the writer uses to open the story - e.g. does it use direct speech? Is a character described? Is the setting described? Is there a 'shock' opening?

b) Think about what it is about the opening that appeals to you and captures your attention.

c) You should have picked out individual words and / or short phrases that you think create a particular effect, feeling or visual impression and explained what they make you think about.

d) You should have described the overall effect that the opening has on you and what effect it has on your imagination.

e) i) You should have identified whether the story is written in the first person or the third person.
   ii) You should have explained the effect that is created through the particular narrative viewpoint used.

f) You should have summed up your overall view on the opening and the impression it creates in your imagination.

Writing Your Own Opening

a)–d) Think carefully about each opening and the effects you want to achieve. You should try to imagine how a reader would respond to what you have written. Would it capture their attention and want to make them read on?

Planning Your Story

a)–h) Think carefully about each part of your story and the ways in which they link together. You have a lot of decisions to make here.

Introducing Characters

a) Try to make your use of direct speech interesting so that it will capture the imagination and attention of the reader in some way.

b) Make sure that your first person narrative exploits the special features of this particular style - perhaps addressin the reader directly or giving them a view on another character or something that has happened.

c) The third person narrative offers different possibilities - perhaps explaining a character's thoughts or giving a third person view of other characters, the event or scene.

CHARACTER AND ATMOSPHERE

Page 10–13

Creating Characters

Here are some possible ideas. Don't worry if you wrote down different points.

a) i) The character is presented as a rough, frightening and violent character. He seems to be a convict judging by the iron on his leg.
   ii) 'I'll cut your throat'; '…a terrible voice.' 'seized me by the chin,' 'glared and growled'.

b) i) Mr Ellis is presented as a frightening and intimidating teacher.
   ii) 'looked like a dirty great thundercloud'; 'monster shoulders like Frankenstein'; 'dead big'.

Making Characters Come to Life

1. a)–h) **Any suitable examples**: Give background information about them; Describe what they look like; Give ideas about their feelings; Through what they say; Through what other characters say about them; Through how they act; Through the beliefs and attitudes they hold; By letting the reader know what's going on in the characters" minds.

2. You are in control with this one. Think carefully about each element of your character in order to build up a character that the reader will find convincing.

Settings

a) The direct speech gives clues that the characters are coming to the end of a long car journey.

b) i) The writer lists different parts of the landscape to give the impression of different sights that can be seen from the car windows as it travels on its journey.
   ii) **Any suitable example**: 'hedges, trees, fields'; 'smooth, milky green sea'.

c) The use of the word 'unrolled' gives a sense of movement as the car travels through countryside and the sights 'unroll' before them.

d) i) Maria imagines the typical things that she remembers of a seaside holiday.

i) 'You have blown up rubber animals'; 'there is sand in your bed at night'.

Atmosphere

1. There are many different kinds of atmosphere to choose from, for example: Happy; Solemn; Exciting; Comfortable; Tense; Frightening; Contented; Creepy

2. When you have decided on the kind of atmosphere that you want to create, think carefully about the vocabulary you use to create a sense of it in the mind of the reader. Words are what create the impression of the atmosphere and in order for your writing to achieve the effects that you want, you need to choose the right words and use them in the right way. You could have used adjectives or adverbs to help make your effect vivid and create the atmosphere you want.

GRAMMAR

Page 14–17

Word Classes

Word Classes	Explanation	Example
Noun	A word that names something	Table
Pronoun	A word used instead of a noun	He, her
Verb	A word that describes an action	Run, think
Adjective	A word that describes a noun	Blue, dark
Adverb	A word that describes a verb	Quickly, hungrily
Conjunction	A word that joins two parts of a sentence together	And, but
Preposition	A word which shows a connection between a noun and the rest of the sentence	On, out, in
Interjection	A word that express an emotion	Oh! Ouch!
Article	Introduces a noun	The, a

Word Classes in Action
a) Noun
b) Verb
c) Preposition
d) Adverb
e) Preposition
f) Conjunction
g) Article
h) Interjection
i) Pronoun
j) Article
k) Noun
l) Preposition
m) Pronoun

n) Adjective
o) Noun

Types of Nouns
a) Proper
b) Collective
c) Abstract
d) Common
e) Proper
f) Abstract
g) Common
h) Common
i) Collective
j) Proper
k) Common
l) Common
m) Common
n) Abstract
o) Abstract
p) Collective
q) Proper
r) Abstract
s) Common
t) Proper
u) Common
v) Abstract
w) Common
x) Common
y) Proper
z) Abstract

Identifying Word Classes
a) His (line 1); They (x2 line 2); They (x2 line 3); Their (line 4); They (line 5); Their (line 6); Them (line 7); They (line 7)
b) To (line 1); At (line 4); To (line 4); From (line 6); To (x2 line 6); To (line 7)
c) And (x2 line 1); And (x2 line 2); But (line 4); Because (line 5); And (line 6); And (line 7)
d) The (x2, definite, line 1); A (indefinite, line 3); The (x2 definite, line 3); An (indefinite, line 4); The (definite, line 4); The (x2 definite, line 5); The (x2 definite, line 6); A (Indefinite, line 7); The (x2 definite, line 7)

AUDIENCE AND PURPOSE

Page 18–21

Purpose
a)–d) You have a wide range of material to choose from here. Make sure you have thought carefully about each kind of writing you have chosen and the purposes for each.

Purpose and Audience
a) i) Mum
   ii) To inform mum that Mandy won't be in for tea, she is going to the cinema with Becky.
b) i) Young children
   ii) To entertain
c) i) General readers interested in history or students studying history.
   ii) To inform

Types of Writing

b) i)–ii) **In any order:** The writing should be suitable for a general audience; it should be laid out as an easy to follow section – perhaps with the use of bullet points to help present the information clearly.

c) i)–ii) **In any order:** the writing should be suitable for a general audience, although it might contain some specialised vocabulary as it's likely the readers would know something about computer games and terms already; the views of the reviewer would need to be clear – perhaps a rating system (for example, stars) might be used to give a quick view of how good the reviewer thought the game was.

d) i)–ii) **In any order:** The writing should give a clear but brief outline of the resort, etc.; information about accommodation, amenities etc. should be clear and easy to understand.

e) i)–ii) **In any order:** Information about the phone should be clear, brief and easy to follow; the design and language used should have impact, capture the reader's attention and be persuasive.

Writing Short Pieces

a)–c) Think carefully about what you want your writing to achieve and use language effectively.

DEVELOPING A POINT OF VIEW

Page 22–26

Points of View

a) i)–v) **In any order:** Rhetorical questions; repetition; use of counter-arguments; warning of effects; use of exclamations

b) i)–v) Think carefully about how you have used each technique.

Fact and Opinion

1. a) Fact
   b) Fact
   c) Opinion
   d) Fact
   e) Opinion
   f) Opinion
   g) Fact
   h) Opinion
   i) Fact
   j) Fact
   k) Opinion
   l) Opinion

2. a) i) i) **Fact:** Many years ago Paul McCartney was a member of The Beatles.
      ii) **Opinion:** He still writes good songs today.
   b) i) **Fact:** Margaret Thatcher was the first female Prime Minister.
      ii) **Opinion:** Did a fantastic job of running the country.
   c) i) **Fact:** Charles I was executed.
      ii) **Opinion:** Because he listened to the advice of fools.
   d) i) **Fact:** Shakespeare wrote Macbeth.
      ii) **Opinion:** It is his best play.
   e) i) **Fact:** Science is an important subject.
      ii) **Opinion:** Easily the most enjoyable.

Writing Fact and Opinion

1. Make sure that your account or description is a factual one, for example check your information such as figures, dates, etc. if necessary.

2. Make sure that your account is based entirely on your own ideas and opinions – try to avoid using factual information.

Writing Techniques

a)–e) **In any order:** Clear statement of the topic and purpose of the letter; the use of a rhetorical question; use of counter-argument; use of exclamation; Warning of consequences

Presenting Your Own Views

a) You should have thought carefully about the topic you have written about – make sure that it is one that you have some views on.

b) Your opening sentence is crucial. It must be effective in capturing the reader's attention.

c) Your opening paragraph should make your point of view clear.

d) Paragraphs one and two should develop your ideas in more detail and bring in evidence or other information to support your view.

e) You should have summed up your ideas and reinforced your point in the conclusion. Try to finish in a way that creates an impact on your reader.

PRESENTING INFORMATION

Page 27–31

Writing to Inform

1. a)-i) **There are many kinds of writing to choose from, for example:** Magazine; Letter; Timetable; Newspaper report; A note; Diary; Information leaflet; Advertisement; Guide book

2. All the kinds of writing you have chosen will have a common purpose – to inform.

Informative Writing

a) heading
b) bold
c) fonts
d) sizes
e) text
f) sub-headings
g) colour
h) bullet
i) italics
j) **In any order:** photographs; diagrams

Presenting Information Effectively

a) Interview
b) Report
c) Fonts
d) Graph
e) Heading
f) Map
g) Photographs
h) Bullet
i) Underlining
j) Diary
k) Letter
l) Brochure

U	C	G	S	Z	S	F	R	U	S	W	V	E	Q	W
S	J	T	S	H	P	A	R	G	O	T	O	H	P	G
Q	O	P	E	F	O	E	B	G	G	R	A	P	H	M
F	Z	R	V	Y	A	S	T	G	T	J	M	K	I	J
L	O	P	E	A	V	P	D	Y	R	A	I	D	W	R
B	A	N	E	P	Y	M	S	F	Y	L	A	D	V	R
U	Z	E	T	V	O	X	Y	V	M	E	W	P	Z	Z
L	G	V	I	S	F	R	E	O	E	T	S	M	A	P
L	O	X	K	V	Y	R	T	Z	N	T	A	O	I	S
E	G	O	I	N	T	E	R	V	I	E	W	T	I	E
T	P	R	C	Z	D	H	G	S	B	R	X	D	D	M
A	K	W	L	H	T	O	I	W	G	Z	H	M	I	H
G	T	H	E	A	D	I	N	G	Q	C	Z	A	P	W
C	S	U	N	D	E	R	L	I	N	I	N	G	D	D
X	T	W	K	N	N	B	R	O	C	H	U	R	E	Y

Creating Effect

a) The name of the falconry centre, its location and that it gives you the experience of seeing hawks.
b) It gives a visual impression of someone flying a hawk to help you know what to expect. The picture of the flying owl also tells you that other birds of prey are there.
c) This draws attention to a rare bird that is at the Centre, which stresses that this is Britain's only Lappett Faced Vulture and that you can meet her. Giving her the name Vera makes her seem a character.
d) Times of opening and the times of the flying displays. The information is clearly presented using large type and there's a visual display of the times of the flying displays.
e) The range of things to see and do. Bullet points are used to present this information clearly.
f) The website address and directions of how to get to the centre.

Designing Your Own Leaflet

- The purpose of your leaflet is to provide information about your resort or attraction – make sure that you have created a positive impression.
- Make sure that your information is clear and easy to understand.
- Draw attention to certain key points and present the ideas clearly.
- You should have used different styles of lettering to create effects and present the information clearly.

- You should have used techniques such as bullet points, illustrations, maps, tables, diagrams, colour, pictures etc. where necessary to make your leaflet more effective.

MEDIA TEXTS

Page 32–35

Newspapers

a)–d) In any order: Regional; Weekend; Weekly; Free

You should have named a specific example of each newspaper and clearly described the content.

Features of a Newspaper

a) columns
b) editor
c) banner
d) copy
e) facts
f) exclusive
g) journalists
h) photographs
i) lead
j) opinions
k) captions

Analysing an Article

a) The eye-catching bold headline – note the play on words, 'I love chew!'. The rest of the headline gives an amusing slant on what has happened.
b) The opening paragraphs introduce the basics of the story.
c) The story is developed with further details and the location.
d) An expert view, which also gives background. Note the use of direct speech here and also the amusing reference to beaver traps: '…beaver traps are in short supply. They don't exactly sell them in B&Q.'
e) The final two paragraphs give more detailed background about the escaped beaver and the article ends with some general background about beavers in England and Wales.

Writing Your Own Newspaper Article

a) Headline – this should be striking and eye-catching.
b) Opening paragraph – this should be clear and let the reader quickly understand what the article is about.
c) Main body – this should develop the storyline in an interesting way using various techniques such as quotation, eye–witness accounts, background information etc.
d) Conclusion – this should end the story in an effective way.

SHAKESPEARE

Page 36–40

Types of Play

1. **Any three suitable examples e.g.:** *Othello; Macbeth; King Lear; Hamlet; Romeo and Juliet; Julius Caesar; Antony and Cleopatra*
2. **Any three suitable examples e.g.:** *A Midsummer Night's Dream; As You Like It; All's Well that Ends Well; Much Ado*

About Nothing; The Merchant of Venice; Twelfth Night

3. **Any three suitable examples e.g.:** Henry IV (part 1); Henry IV (part 2); Henry V; Richard II; Richard III

4. **Any three suitable examples e.g.:** The Tempest; The Winter's Tale; Cymbeline

5. a) Last plays
   b) Fantasy and magic

Shakespeare's Comedies

1. A Shakespearean Tragedy ends with the death of the main character (other characters die during the play and often at the end too.) Shakespearean comedies end happily, often with marriages involved.

2. a) Characters meet and fall in love.
   b) Things go wrong and complications arise – there's often confusion, frequently involving mistaken identity or disguise.
   c) A climax is reached, the problems are sorted out and the confusion is cleared up.
   d) The play ends happily with the lovers together; often it ends in a marriage or marriages.

Soliloquies

1. A speech made by a character when they're alone on stage or when they seem to be talking directly to the audience.

2. a)–d) **In any order:** What the character's thinking; What the character's feeling; What the characters intend to do; Give information that other characters don't know.

3. Iago wants to take Casio's place and is prepared to use anything it takes to do this. He's going to tell Othello that Cassio is paying too much attention to his wife. Othello (the Moor) is so trusting he will believe this. Othello thinks that men are honest just because they seem to be so. Iago has struck upon his plan. Iago thinks that Othello is easily led.

Examining Soliloquies

1. a) Make sure that you are clear who is speaking.
   b) Clearly explain where the soliloquy comes in the action of the play.
   c) Make sure you understand exactly what the audience learns from the soliloquy.
   d) Clearly explain what the soliloquy tells you about the character.

2. a)–c) For each of the images you have chosen identify what kind of image it is accurately and explain carefully and in as much detail as you can the effect created by the image.

Imagery in Shakespeare

1. a) i) A metaphor compares one thing with another by saying that one thing actually is the thing it is compared to.
      ii) **Any suitable example e.g.:** All the world's a stage.
   b) i) A simile compares one thing to another by using the word 'like' or 'as'.
      ii) **Any suitable example e.g.:** As fast as lightning; As blind as a bat.
   c) i) Personification is when an object or something not human is given human characteristics.
      ii) **Any suitable example e.g.:** The flowers turned their faces towards the sun.

2. a) i) Simile
      ii) The battle was very close. Both armies struggled, neither gaining the upper hand, like two exhausted swimmers clinging to each other, preventing each other from swimming.
   b) i) Personification
      ii) The Prince will hide his true, noble nature like the sun, who allows the clouds to conceal his beauty from the world so that when the clouds pass and the sun breaks through, his radiance creates more impact. The sun and clouds are described as if they're living beings.

READING POETRY

Page 41–45

Reading Poetry

1. a) i) Created by the repetition of words with the same consonant.
      ii) **Any suitable example, e.g:** Big brown bear
   b) i) Like alliteration, but involves the repetition of vowel sounds.
      ii) **Any suitable example, e.g:** Look at the cook book.
   c) i) When a word sounds like the sound it describes.
      ii) **Any suitable example, e.g:** Boom! Bang!

2. a) Simile
   b) Simile
   c) Personification

You should have explained clearly your own response to each image.

Rhyme and Rhythm

1. a) ABAB, CDCD
   b) The rhyme scheme links words that go together, which adds emphasis to them, e.g. crocodile / Nile; tails / scale; grin / fishes in; claws / jaws. It also works with the rhythm of the poem to create a humorous effect.

2. a) The rhythm pattern creates a repetitive effect.
   b) It suggests the drumming of horse hooves as they charge down the valley.

Writing a Poem of Your Own

1. You should have considered:
   - the subject matter of your poem
   - the title
   - whether or not a rhyme scheme will be used – this will be linked to the overall effect you want your poem to achieve
   - imagery – again this is linked to the effects you want to create

2. a)–c) You should have explained, in as much detail as you can, the choices you made and why you made them.

Studying a Poem

a)–e) Think about your responses to these carefully. There are no right or wrong answers. Write about what the poem means to you.

Writing About a Poem

a)–e) You should have considered the key elements of the poem:
   - content
   - tone
   - rhyme

- rhythm
- imagery

PUNCTUATION

Page 46–49

Kinds of Speech

1. a) Direct
   b) Direct
   c) Indirect
   d) Indirect
   e) Direct
2. a)-c) Make sure you check your answers carefully.
3. a)-c) Make sure you check your answers carefully.

Writing Direct Speech

1. a)–c) Check that you have punctuated your speech correctly.
2. Germaine had run ahead of the rest and so reached the shop first. He called back to the others, 'Hurry up. I'm hungry and Matt has all the money.' 'You'll just have to wait for us. We're not all Olympic standard runners like you,' said Mandy. Germaine laughed and said, 'You should cut down on the burgers and chips and then you might be able to move a bit faster than a snail's pace.'
Mandy and the others finally reached the shop panting heavily and Jo complained, 'I have not moved as quickly as this since I nearly missed the last bus after I'd been to the cinema.' Germaine said, 'It is all worth it. At least the shop is still open. The owner was just about to close and we would have missed it if we had not moved fast.'

Punctuation and Speech

'Have you anything to say?' demanded Squeers again: giving his right arm two or three flourishes to try its power and suppleness. 'Stand a little out of the way, Mrs Squeers, my dear; I've hardly got room enough.'
'Spare me, sir!' cried Smike.
'Oh! That's all, is it?' said Squeers. 'Yes, I'll flog you within an inch of your life, and spare you that.'
'Ha, ha, ha,' laughed Mrs Squeers, 'that's a good 'un!'
'I was driven to do it,' said Smike faintly; and casting another imploring look about him.
'Driven to do it, were you?' said Squeers. 'Oh! It wasn't your fault; it was mine, I suppose-eh?'
'A nasty, ungrateful, pig-headed, brutish, obstinate, sneaking dog,' exclaimed Mrs Squeers, taking Smike's head under her arm, and administering a cuff at every epithet; 'what does he mean by that?'
'Stand aside, my dear,' replied Squeers. 'We'll try and find out.' Mrs Squeers, being out of breath with her exertions, complied. Squeers caught the boy firmly in his grip; one desperate cut had fallen on his body – he was wincing from the lash and uttering a scream of pain – it was raised again, and again about to fall – when Nicholas Nickleby, suddenly starting up, cried 'Stop!' in a voice that made the rafters ring.

Play Scripts

1. a) False
   b) False
   c) True
   d) True

2. *(Oliver, rising from the table, advances to the master with basin and spoon in hand)*
OLIVER: Please, sir, I want some more.
(The master looks stupefied with astonishment and clings to the copper. The assistants are paralysed with amazement and the boys look fearful)
MASTER: (faintly) What?
OLIVER: Please, sir, I want some more.
(The master aims a blow at Oliver and, grabbing his arms, shouts for the Beadle.)
(In the Boardroom. Mr Bumble rushes in highly excited)
MR BUMBLE: Mr Limpkins, I beg your pardon sir! Oliver Twist has asked for more!
(Everyone jumps and looks horrified)
Mr LIMPKINS: For more?! Compose yourself Mr Bumble, and answer me distinctly. Do I understand that he asked for more, after he had eaten the supper allotted by the dietary?
MR BUMBLE: He did, sir.
GENTLEMAN: That boy will be hung. I know that boy will be hung.

SPELLING

Page 50–53

1. a) Boxes
   b) Wolves
   c) Tattoos
   d) Centuries
   e) Teeth
   f) Qualities
   g) Mementoes
   h) Laboratories
   i) Ties
   j) Buoys
   k) Handkerchiefs
   l) Halves
   m) Zoos
   n) Opportunities
   o) Zeroes or zeros
   p) People
   q) Photos
   r) Potatoes
   s) Giraffes
   t) Mottos

Plurals

1. a) hutches; burrows
   b) boxes; fireworks
   c) wolves; people
   d) trolleys; groceries
   e) buoys
   f) galaxies; planets
   g) heroes
   h) brushes; scissors
   i) knives; dishes
   j) volcanoes
   k) bunches; vases
   l) solos; judges
   m) churches; haloes
   n) calves; lives

Homophones

a) Word 1: Stationery
   Word 2: Stationary
b) Word 1: Carat
   Word 2: Carrot
c) Word 1: Seen
   Word 2: Scene
d) Word 1: Bear
   Word 2: Bare
e) Word 1: Rap
   Word 2: Wrap
f) Word 1: Steel
   Word 2: Steal
g) Word 1: Miner
   Word 2: Minor
h) Word 1: Waste
   Word 2: Waist
i) Word 1: Flower
   Word 2: Flour

Check that you have used the correct spellings in each of your sentences.

Commonly Confused Words

a) there; their; they're
b) to; two; too
c) here; hear
d) stationery; stationary
e) principal; principle
f) currants; current; current; current
g) whether; weather
h) programme; program
i) seems; seams
j) would; wood

READING FOR MEANING

Page 54–56

Types of Non-fiction

1. a)–e) There are a range of texts you might have chosen. Make sure you've explained carefully why you might read each of your choices. For example, types of non-fiction text: A newspaper report on a football match. Reason you might read it: To find out what happened in the match, opinions on how the teams played etc.

2. a)–d) In any order: Content; The way language is used; The way information is presented; Your own thoughts and ideas about it

Writing Your Own Piece of Non-fiction

a) You should have chosen an appropriate title.
b) Your introductory paragraph should be interesting and should capture the reader's attention while at the same time focusing on the topic.
c) You should have developed your ideas clearly and logically.
d) The piece should be rounded off with an effective and relevant concluding paragraph.

Comprehension

a) 1348
b) Bubonic plague
c) i)-ii) **In any order:** A sailor who had caught the disease; The fleas on rats that lived on the ships.
d) China
e) Between 1348 and 1349
f) About 2,500,000
g) About 7,500,000
h) In towns where living conditions were dirty and ideal for rats and their fleas to live in.

ACKNOWLEDGEMENTS

The author and publisher are grateful to the copyright holders for permission to use quoted materials and images.

Every effort has been made to trace copyright holders and obtain their permission for the use of copyright material. The authors and publishers will gladly receive information enabling them to rectify any error or omission in subsequent editions. All facts are correct at time of going to press.

Published by Lonsdale
An imprint of HarperCollins Publishers
77–85 Fulham Palace Road
London W6 8JB

© 2009 Lonsdale, an imprint of HarperCollins Publishers

ISBN 9781906415938

01/040211

British Library Cataloguing in Publication Data.

A CIP record of this book is available from the British Library.

Book concept and development: Helen Jacobs
Commissioning Editor: Rebecca Skinner
Author: Steven Croft
Project Editor: Robert Dean
Cover Design: Angela English
Inside Concept Design: Helen Jacobs and Sarah Duxbury
Text Design and Layout: Little Red Dog Design
Artwork: Lonsdale

Work out the answers to the clues below, then find them in the word search. All the words are either types of writing or things that can be used to help present information effectively.

U	C	G	S	Z	S	F	R	U	S	W	V	E	Q	W
S	J	T	S	H	P	A	R	G	O	T	O	H	P	G
Q	O	P	E	F	O	E	B	G	G	R	A	P	H	M
F	Z	R	V	Y	A	S	T	G	T	J	M	K	I	J
L	O	P	E	A	V	P	D	Y	R	A	I	D	W	R
B	A	N	E	P	Y	M	S	F	Y	L	A	D	V	R
U	Z	E	T	V	O	X	Y	V	M	E	W	P	Z	Z
L	G	V	I	S	F	R	E	O	E	T	S	M	A	P
L	O	X	K	V	Y	R	T	Z	N	T	A	O	I	S
E	G	O	I	N	T	E	R	V	I	E	W	T	I	E
T	P	R	C	Z	D	H	G	S	B	R	X	D	D	M
A	K	W	L	H	T	O	I	W	G	Z	H	M	I	H
G	T	H	E	A	D	I	N	G	Q	C	Z	A	P	W
C	S	U	N	D	E	R	L	I	N	I	N	G	D	D
X	T	W	K	N	N	B	R	O	C	H	U	R	E	Y

a) A celebrity might give one of these to a magazine.

b) Your parents might receive one of these about you.

c) Letters with style.

d) Diagram showing proportions; bar or pie.

e) The first thing you read in a newspaper story.

f) Find your way with this.

g) Snap these.

h) What kind of point?

i) Underneath words.

j) A personal written daily entry.

k) Written way of complaining.

l) You could find your holiday in one of these.

Creating Effect

Look at the following leaflet, then answer the questions on the effects various parts of it create.

a) What information do the heading and sub-headings give you?

b) What effect do you think the picture creates?

c) Why do you think Vera is so named and details are given about her?

d) What information is given here and how is it displayed?

Designing Your Own Leaflet (Cont.)

e) What two types of information are given here and what technique is used to present it?

_____

_____

f) What information are you given at the end of the leaflet?

_____

_____

Designing Your Own Leaflet

Design your own information leaflet promoting a holiday resort, fun park or other attraction that you know well.

Draft the text and layout for your leaflet below.

Media Texts

List five different kinds of newspapers. Give the title and briefly describe the content you might find in each one. An example has been done for you.

Kind of newspaper: Daily

Specific example: Daily Mirror

Content: News, Sport, Entertainment, Cartoons, Horoscopes, Puzzles, Television

a) Kind of newspaper:

Specific example:

Content:

b) Kind of newspaper:

Specific example:

Content:

c) Kind of newspaper:

Specific example:

Content:

d) Kind of newspaper:

Specific example:

Content:

Features of a Newspaper

Choose the correct words from the options given to complete the sentences below.

blocks	copy	main	ideas	columns
writing	titles	captions	journalists	photographs
editor	manager	facts	writers	inclusive
banner	lead	heading	exclusive	centre
opinions	type	bold	tabloid	reviews

a) The text in newspapers is normally laid out in _____.

b) The person who decides on what goes into a newspaper is called the _____.

c) The front page headline is called a _____ headline.

d) The text written for a newspaper is often called the _____.

e) Newspaper reports are usually based on _____.

f) A story that only one newspaper has information about is called an _____ story.

g) People who write the stories that are published in newspapers are called

_____.

h) Sometimes _____ are used to illustrate newspaper stories.

i) The main story in a newspaper is called the _____ story.

j) As well as facts, newspaper reports might also contain some _____.

k) Photographs or illustrations usually have _____ to explain what they are.

Analysing an Article

Identify the effects created by each of the following parts of the newspaper report.

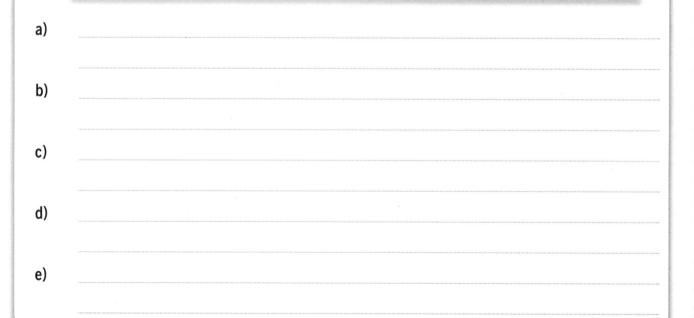

a)

I LOVE CHEW! LOVELORN BEAVER FELLS TREES IN FRANTIC HUNT FOR MATE

b)

FELLED trees along a riverbank puzzled countryside lovers for days - until a wildlife expert noticed teeth marks on the branches.

Yesterday a hunt was under way for a beaver which has left a trail of destruction as it searches for a mate.

The male rodent, which weighs six stone, fled a farm enclosure by clambering over an electric fence and scrambling more than 20 miles.

c)

The eager beaver has gnawed its way through a swathe of trees on a one-and a-half-mile stretch of riverbank in a desperate bid to build the perfect dam to attract a female.

It fled its enclosure from a farm in Lifton, Devon, six weeks ago with two females who were soon recaptured.

But the male beaver is still searching for a mate and is hiding out near the picturesque village of Gunnislake, in Cornwall.

It is trying to build the perfect dam to attract a mate, but cannot form its love-nest properly because the River Tamar is too wide and fast-flowing for one beaver to tame.

Locals began to notice fallen trees bearing the markings of beaver teeth -

but experts were baffled, as the animals have been extinct in England for 800 years. Then the beaver's owner Derek Gow came forward to reveal the identity of the culprit and is now laying a series of humane traps to capture it.

Mr Gow, 43, a conservationist, says the "docile and family-orientated" beaver is living on a one-and-a-half-mile stretch of the River Tamar.

d)

He said: "I know where it is - that's not the problem. Beavers haven't lived here since the 13th century so beaver traps are in short supply. They don't exactly sell them at B&Q."

"We've made our own traps out of steel and aluminium. Wood is no good for a beaver trap for obvious reasons."

"The trap contains female scent which we think may work because he must be lonely and searching for a partner."

e)

The eight-year-old beaver weighs 40 kilograms and was brought to the UK five years ago from Bavaria. It is a vegetarian and stays within 50 yards of the water.

Beavers were hunted to extinction in England and Wales during the 12th century. They were captured for their fur and throat glands, which were believed to have medicinal properties.

a) ....

b) ....

c) ....

d) ....

e) ....

Writing Your Own Newspaper Article

1 Write your own newspaper article or story, no longer than 120 words.

Think of an idea on which to base your article. Use the plan below to structure your 'copy'.

a) Headline (and sub-headline if used)

....

b) Opening paragraph

....

....

c) Main body of article (two to three paragraphs)

....

....

....

....

....

....

....

....

....

d) Conclusion

....

....

....

2 Make a note of any ideas you have for an illustration / picture you might use to illustrate your article and say why you would use it.

....

....

....

Shakespeare

1 List three tragedies written by Shakespeare.

a) ....

b) ....

c) ....

2 List three comedies written by Shakespeare.

a) ....

b) ....

c) ....

3 List three history plays written by Shakespeare

a) ....

b) ....

c) ....

4 List three romance plays written by Shakespeare.

a) ....

b) ....

c) ....

5 a) What are the romance plays also known as?

....

b) What often features in Shakespeare romance plays?

....

Shakespeare's Comedies

1 Explain the differences between a Shakespearean comedy and a Shakespearean tragedy.

2 The stories of Shakespeare's comedies are structured in a particular way.

Explain what happens in the four main stages of development of a typical Shakespearean comedy.

a) Stage 1

b) Stage 2

c) Stage 3

d) Stage 4

Soliloquies

1 What is a soliloquy?

_____

_____

2 List four things an audience can learn from a soliloquy.

a) _____

b) _____

c) _____

d) _____

3 Read the following soliloquy extract from _Othello_. It is spoken by Iago, Othello's trusted personal servant. Iago hates Othello and is jealous that Cassio has been given a promotion that Iago wanted himself.

> Cassio's a proper man: let me see now:
> To get his place and to plume up my will
> In double knavery - How, how? Let's see: -
> After some time, to abuse Othello's ear
> That he is too familiar with his wife.
> He hath a person and a smooth dispose
> To be suspected, framed to make women false.
> The Moor is of a free and open nature,
> That thinks men honest that but seem to be so,
> And will as tenderly be led by the nose
> As asses are.
> I have't. It is engender'd. Hell and night
> Must bring this monstrous birth to the world's light.

Note down all the things that you learn from this soliloquy.

_____

_____

_____

_____

_____

Examining Soliloquies

1 Look at a Shakespeare play that you have studied and choose a soliloquy from it.

a) Who speaks the soliloquy?

b) Where does the soliloquy appear in the play?

c) What is revealed to the audience in the soliloquy?

d) What does the soliloquy tell you about the character who's speaking?

2 Find three examples of imagery in your chosen play. For each image write about the...

- kind of image it is
- effect created by the image.

a) Image 1:

b) Image 2:

c) Image 3:

Imagery in Shakespeare

1 Explain the meaning of the following terms and give an example of each one.

a) i) Metaphor:

    ii) Example:

b) i) Simile:

    ii) Example:

c) i) Personification:

    ii) Example:

2 Look at the following examples of the use of imagery in Shakespeare's plays. Explain what kind of imagery is being used in each one and describe how the imagery works.

a) A soldier in *Macbeth* describes a battle between two armies:

> Doubtful it stood;
> As two spent swimmers, that do cling together
> And choke their art.

    i) Kind of imagery:

    ii) What the imagery means:

b) In *Henry IV*, Prince Hal explains how he intends to show himself in a good light:

> Yet herein will I imitate the sun,
> Who doth permit the base contagious clouds
> To smother up his beauty from the world,
> That, when he please again to be himself,
> Being wanted, he may be more wonder'd at,
> By breaking through the foul and ugly mists
> Of vapours that did seem to strangle him

    i) Kind of imagery:

    ii) What the imagery means:

Reading Poetry

1 Explain the meaning of the following terms and give an example of each one.

a) **i)** Alliteration: ....

....

ii) Example: ....

b) **i)** Assonance: ....

....

ii) Example: ....

c) **i)** Onomatopoeia: ....

....

ii) Example: ....

2 Read the following lines which are from various poems. Identify what kind of imagery is used in each one and describe what effects you think it creates.

a) She walks in beauty, like the night
Of cloudless climes and starry skies;

Kind of imagery: ....

Effects: ....

....

b) Love struck into his life
Like a hawk into a dovecote.

Kind of imagery: ....

Effects: ....

....

c) The wind stood up, and gave a shout;
He whistled on his fingers, and
Kicked the withered leaves about,

Kind of imagery: ....

Effects: ....

....

Rhyme and Rhythm

1 Read the following poem by Lewis Carroll.

> **The Crocodile**
> How doth the little crocodile
> Improve his shining tail,
> And pour the waters of the Nile
> On every golden scale!
>
> How cheerfully he seems to grin,
> How neatly spreads his claws
> And welcomes little fishes in,
> With gently smiling jaws!

a) Identify the rhyme scheme.

....

b) What effects do you think the rhyme creates?

....

....

2 Look at the following stanzas from Tennyson's *The Charge of the Light Brigade*.

> Half a league, half a league,
> Half a league onward,
> All in the valley of Death
> Rode the six hundred.
> "Forward the Light Brigade!
> Charge for the guns!" he said.
> Into the valley of Death
> Rode the six hundred.
>
> 'Forward, the Light Brigade!'
> Was there a man dismay'd?
> Not tho' the soldier knew
> Some one had blunder'd.
> Theirs not to make reply,
> Theirs not to reason why,
> Theirs but to do and die.
> Into the valley of Death
> Rode the six hundred.

a) How would you describe the rhythm in this poem?

....

....

b) What kind of 'feel' does the rhythm give to the poem?

....

Writing a Poem of Your Own

1 Write a poem of your own about anything you want. Your poem should…

- have a title
- be 10–12 lines long
- have a rhyme scheme
- contain three or more images (one of these should be an aural image).

2 **a)** Explain why you chose to write about your choice of topic.

b) Explain why you chose the rhyme scheme and what you think it adds to your poem.

c) Explain why you chose your images and describe the effects you wanted them to create.

Image 1:

Image 2:

Image 3:

Studying a Poem

Carefully read Thomas Hardy's *Snow in the Suburbs* poem below, then write your own response to it.

Every branch big with it,
Bent every twig with it;
Every fork like a white web-foot;
Every street and pavement mute:
Some flakes have lost their way, and grope back upward, when
Meeting those meandering down they turn and descend again.
The palings are glued together like a wall,
And there is no waft of wind with the fleecy fall.

A sparrow enters the tree,
Whereon immediately
A snow-lump thrice his own slight size
Descends on him and showers his head and eyes,
And overturns him,
And near inurns him,
And lights on a lower twig, when its brush
Starts off a volley of other lodging lumps with a rush.

The steps are a blanched slope,
Up which, with feeble hope,
A black cat comes, wide-eyed and thin;
And we take him in.

a) This is a poem about...

b) The opening two lines are effective because...

c) The simile in line three compared...

d) This simile helped me to imagine...

e) Another simile is used near the end of the stanza and I felt this was effective because...

Writing About a Poem

Choose a poem you have read either in class or elsewhere. Write about your thoughts and feelings on the poem.

a) Why did you choose the poem?

_____

_____

_____

b) What is the poem about?

_____

_____

_____

c) How does the poet use language in the poem?

_____

_____

_____

d) Choose three examples of words, phrases or images the poet uses and write about the effects these create.

_____

_____

_____

e) Write about your overall impression and feelings about the poem.

_____

_____

_____

_____

Punctuation

Kinds of Speech

1 Say whether the following sentences contain **direct** or **indirect** speech.

a) 'Hi!' said Harry. 'Are you coming round to my house tonight?' ....

b) 'I hope you're joking,' said Helen, 'or I might be a little bit annoyed.' ....

c) Elvis asked Wayne if he had finished his homework and handed it in. ....

d) Mark wondered what had happened to his best shirt as he poked his finger through a large hole. ....

e) 'Go on, have one. You know you want to,' urged Sophie. ....

2 Write three sentences of your own in **direct** speech.

a) ....

....

....

b) ....

....

....

c) ....

....

....

3 Write three sentences of your own in **indirect** speech

a) ....

....

....

b) ....

....

....

c) ....

....

Writing Direct Speech

1 When writing direct speech, the part telling you who's speaking can come at the beginning, the middle or the end of the words spoken.

Write an example of each kind, making sure you put all your punctuation marks in the right places.

a) Beginning

b) Middle

c) End

2 The following passage is written in indirect speech. Rewrite it so that it's in direct speech.

Germaine had run ahead of the rest and so reached the shop first. He called back to the others shouting to them to hurry up because he was hungry and Matt had all the money. Mandy told him he would just have to wait for them because they were not all Olympic standard runners like he was. Germaine laughed and told them they should cut down on the burgers and chips and then they might be able to move a little bit faster than snail's pace. Mandy and the others finally reached the shop, panting heavily, and Jo complained she had not moved as quickly as that since she nearly missed the last bus home after a night out at the cinema. Germaine told them that it was all worth it though because at least the shop was still open, and as the owner was just about to close up, they would have missed it if they had not moved fast.

Punctuation and Speech

Rewrite the following passage, putting in all the correct speech punctuation and using the right speech layout.

Have you anything to say demanded Squeers again: giving his right arm two or three flourishes to try its power and suppleness. Stand a little out of the way, Mrs Squeers, my dear; I've hardly got room enough. Spare me, sir cried Smike. Oh! that's all, is it said Squeers. yes, I'll flog you within an inch of your life, and spare you that. Ha, ha, ha, laughed Mrs Squeers, that's a good 'un! I was driven to do it said Smike faintly; and casting another imploring look about him. Driven to do it, were you said Squeers. Oh! it wasn't your fault; it was mine, I suppose-eh? A nasty, ungrateful, pig-headed, brutish, obstinate, sneaking dog exclaimed Mrs Squeers, taking Smike's head under her arm, and administering a cuff at every epithet; what does he mean by that? Stand aside, my dear replied Squeers. We'll try and find out. Mrs Squeers, being out of breath with her exertions, complied. Squeers caught the boy firmly in his grip; one desperate cut had fallen on his body - he was wincing from the lash and uttering a scream of pain - it was raised again, and again about to fall - when Nicholas Nickleby, suddenly starting up, cried Stop! in a voice that made the rafters ring.

From *Nicholas Nickleby* by Charles Dickens

Play Scripts

1 Say whether the following sentences are **true** or **false**.

   a) Speech marks are used when writing play scripts. ....

   b) The speakers' names are separated from the spoken part by semi-colons. ....

   c) The speech for each character begins with a capital letter. ....

   d) Stage directions are usually in italics and brackets. ....

2 Rewrite the following extract into play script form.

> 'Please, sir, I want some more.'
>
> The master was a fat, healthy man; but he turned very pale. He gazed in stupefied astonishment on the small rebel for some seconds, and then clung for support to the copper. The assistants were paralysed with wonder; the boys with fear.
>
> 'What!' said the master at length, in a faint voice.
>
> 'Please, sir,' replied Oliver, 'I want some more.'
>
> The master aimed a blow at Oliver's head with the ladle; pinioned him in his arm; and shrieked aloud for the beadle.
>
> The board were sitting in solemn conclave, when Mr. Bumble rushed into the room in great excitement, and addressing the gentleman in the high chair, said, 'Mr. Limbkins, I beg your pardon, sir! Oliver Twist has asked for more!'
>
> There was a general start. Horror was depicted on every countenance.
>
> 'For more!' said Mr. Limbkins. 'Compose yourself, Bumble, and answer me distinctly. Do I understand that he asked for more, after he had eaten the supper allotted by the dietary?'
>
> 'He did, sir,' replied Bumble.
>
> 'That boy will be hung,' said the gentleman in the white waistcoat. 'I know that boy will be hung.'
>
> From *Oliver Twist* by Charles Dickens

Spelling

Write the plural of each of the following singular words in the boxes below. Remember to check that you have spelt each one correctly.

Singular	Plural
Box	a) Boxes ✓
Wolf	b) Wolves ✓
Tattoo	c) Tattoos ✓
Century	d) Centuries ✓
Tooth	e) ~~mooteen~~ Teeth ✓
Quality	f) Qualities ✓
Memento	g) Mementoes ✓
Laboratory	h) Laboratories ✓
Tie	i) Ties ✓
Buoy	j) Buoys ✓
Handkerchief	k) Handkerchieves
Half	l) Halves ✓
Zoo	m) Zoos ✓
Opportunity	n) Opportunities ✓
Zero	o) Zeros ✓
Person	p) people ✓
Photo	q) Photos ✓
Potato	r) Potatoes ✓
Giraffe	s) Giraffes ✓
Motto	t) Mottos ✓

Plurals

Fill in the missing words to complete the following sentences. The missing words are all plural forms of common words.

(hutches)

a) Pet rabbits are often kept in h uts , but in the wild they live in
   b urrows .

b) Dad bought two big b oxes of f ireworks for Bonfire Night.

c) A pack of w olves were howling in the forest as the small group of
   people huddled round the camp fire.

d) Both shopping t rolleys were completely full of g roceries .

e) The captain turned to starboard and carefully steered the ship between the two
   b uoys .

f) The Starship Enterprise crew discovered many new g alaxies and landed on many
   strange p lanets .

g) Mickey and Michaela were h eroes after they pulled the child from the water.

h) She rinsed her paint b rushes in clean water and trimmed the paper with her
   s cissors .

i) Chefs always keep their k nives sharp as this helps them when preparing
   various d inners . dishes

j) V olcanoes can be very dangerous when they erupt.

k) The wallpaper had colourful patterns on it and there were b unches of flowers in
   v ases on every window sill.

solos
l) The girl played two s ongs on her flute and impressed the
   j udges very much.

haloes

m) The walls of c hurches often have paintings of angels with h alos
   above their heads.

n) The cow gave birth to two c alves and the vet managed to save both their
   l ives .

Homophones

Use the following clues to work out the homophones, then write a sentence for each one using the words correctly.

a) Word 1: Writing materials _Stationery_ ✓

Word 2: Not moving _stationary_ ✓

Word 1 sentence: _My stationery must include a pen and rubber._

Word 2 sentence: _The train was ~~stationery~~ Stationary_

b) Word 1: The weight by which precious stones are measured _carats I measure my sto_

Word 2: A vegetable _Carrots. ~~I prefer carrots stick to boiled carrots.~~_

Word 1 sentence: _I measure my Stones in carats._

Word 2 sentence: _I prefer carrots when they are boiled._

c) Word 1: Noticed, observed _Seen_ ✓

Word 2: The place or setting of a story, for example _Scene_ ✓

Word 1 sentence: _____

Word 2 sentence: _____

d) Word 1: To support, hold up or carry ~~B~~ BEAR

Word 2: Uncovered ~~Beare Bee~~ BARE

Word 1 sentence: _____

Word 2 sentence: _____

e) Word 1: A sharp blow or knock _rap_ ✓

Word 2: To cover with paper and tape _Wrap_ ✓

Word 1 sentence: _____

Word 2 sentence: _____

f) Word 1: A kind of hard metal _steel_ ✓

Word 2: To take without permission _steal_ ✓

Word 1 sentence: _His teeth were made of steel_

Word 2 sentence: _~~~~ "Do not steal" said the police_

g) Word 1: Someone who extracts coal out of the earth _miner_ ✓

Word 2: Of lesser importance _Minor_ ✓

Word 1 sentence: _____

Word 2 sentence: _____

Homophones (Cont.)

h) Word 1: Something worthless, rubbish, refuse _waste_

Word 2: Middle of the human body _waist_

Word 1 sentence: _____

Word 2 sentence: _____

i) Word 1: It grows in the garden _flower_ ✓

Word 2: Used in baking _flour_ ✓

Word 1 sentence: _____

Word 2 sentence: _____

Commonly Confused Words

Circle the correct option in the following sentences, which contain commonly confused words.

a) **They're / Their / There** are two main characters in the story and **they're /their/ there** names are Jill and Saroya. The writer goes into great detail to make sure that **they're** / their / there very well–rounded characters.

b) I have **too / two / to** finish these **too / two / to** questions **too** / two / to.

c) Come over **hear / here** so I can **hear** / here what you're saying.

d) The lorry, which was transporting **stationery** / stationary, was **stationery** / stationary at the traffic lights.

e) The **principle / principal** of the college said that she would resign as a matter of **principle** / principal.

f) The ship, carrying a cargo of **currants** / currents, was swept away from the quay by the strong **currant** / current. At the same time, the ship suffered a power failure, so there was no electrical **currant** / current to power the emergency steering. The whole incident was reported on a news and **currant** / current affairs programme that evening.

g) I couldn't decide **whether** / weather to go for a walk or not because the **whether** / weather was so bad.

h) Yesterday I watched a TV **programme** / program about a new computer **programme** / program.

i) It **seams** / seems that you have sewn these **seams** / seems wrong.

j) **Would** / Wood you walk home with me through the dark **would** / wood?

programme _program_

Reading for Meaning

Types of Non-fiction

1 List five types of non-fiction texts you might come across as part of your everyday life and say why you might read each one.

Type of Non-fiction Text	Reason You Might Read It
a)	
b)	
c)	
d)	
e)	

2 Name four things that you should think about when you read a non-fiction text.

a)

b)

c)

d)

Writing Your Own Piece of Non-fiction

Choose a topic on which to base your own piece of non-fiction writing. You could choose, for example, a hobby, a famous person or celebrity, or a particular issue such as global warming.

Use the following to help you structure your work.

a) The title and topic of your piece.

b) Your introductory paragraph.

c) The main section of your piece of writing (two to three paragraphs).

d) Concluding paragraph to round the piece off.

Comprehension

Read this passage carefully and answer the questions that follow.

Causes of the Black Death

In 1348 people started dying of a disease. It was bubonic plague, now known as the Black Death. In 1894 Scientists discovered that the plague was caused by a germ, which lived on fleas on black rats. When the rats died, the fleas moved onto humans.

It is thought that the disease originally came from China and was spread to Europe by merchants. Historians think the disease was either brought over to England by a sailor who had caught the disease or by rats that lived in the cargo on the ships.

During the Medieval period, people didn't know about the existence of germs and so there were many theories about the cause of the disease. Some people thought the Black Death started in the East when frogs, lizards, snakes and scorpions fell out of the sky, followed by thunder, lightning and fire. Most thought that it had been sent by God to punish people for sins such as gambling, swearing, money lending, fighting and adultery. Many people prayed for forgiveness from God, and one group, which became known as the 'flagellants' even whipped themselves to try to win God's forgiveness.

Between 1348 and 1349 the Black Death spread throughout England and killed about 2,500,000 people - nearly a third of the population. It spread very quickly in towns because they were crowded and dirty, and there was lots of rubbish for the rats to feed on.

a) When did people in England first start dying of the Black Death? ....

b) What is another name for the Black Death? ....

c) Give two possible ways that the disease was carried to this country.

    i) ....

    ii) ....

d) Where did the disease originally come from? ....

e) When did the disease spread throughout England?

....

f) Approximately how many people did the disease kill? ....

g) What was the population of England at this time? ....

h) Where did the disease spread especially quickly and why?

....

....